The Long Bl

The focus in this book is on the graphemes

ue, u-e, ew

blue

June cute tube

huge useful

grew chewing

The plants in the garden at Follifoot
Farm grew tall and strong in the
summer month of June.

1

A cute rabbit was chewing the carrot tops. She saw a long blue tube. It went all the way to the strawberries.

A cheeky blackbird was pecking the
strawberries. He saw the long blue
tube. It went all the way to some
huge cabbages.

Kevin was digging in the soil among the cabbages. He saw the long blue tube. It went all the way to the roses.

Kevin went to the roses. Wellington was sitting next to the tube. He looked as if he was waiting for something to happen.

Kevin stood over the tube and looked at it closely. Ah! The tube had holes all the way along it.

Just then, water shot out of the

holes all the way along the tube.

Kevin jumped up in surprise.

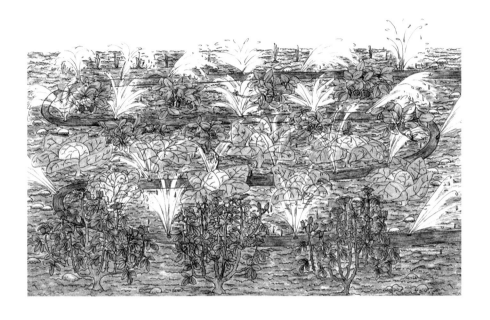

The water fell on the carrots, the
ripe strawberries, the huge cabbages
and the roses. Ah! The tube was for
watering the plants.

The water fell on the cute rabbit
and the cheeky blackbird too. They
had a lovely cool shower from it.

Kevin and Wellington had a drink of water from the tube. They both thought it was a very useful long blue tube.

Vowel graphemes

ai/ay/a-e:	waiting way cabbages
ee:	cheeky
i-e:	surprise ripe
o-e:	roses over closely holes
ue/ew/u-e:	blue grew chewing June
	cute tube huge useful
oo:	too cool
oo:	looked stood Follifoot
ow/ou:	shower out
or:	for
ar:	garden Farm
er:	summer over water shower
ir:	blackbird
ur:	surprise
aw:	saw strawberries
oi:	soil